Usborne English Readers

Level 2

Jason
and the
Argonauts

Retold by Andy Prentice

Illustrated by Natalie Dombois

English language consultant: Peter Viney

Contents

You can listen to the story online here:
www.usborneenglishreaders.com/
jasonandtheargonauts

Jason was the son of King Aeson of Thessaly, but he never knew his father. His uncle, Pelias, killed Aeson when Jason was only a baby. Pelias became king, and Jason had to leave Thessaly. He grew up poor and angry, far away from home.

When he was eighteen years old, Jason came back to Thessaly. He walked slowly into the palace. He was alone, but he was so tall and brave that nobody tried to stop him.

"Who are you?" asked King Pelias.

"I am Jason, son of Aeson," Jason said quietly. "Thessaly is my country, not yours. I am the true king."

His uncle was frightened of this strong young man, so he tried to trick him.

"You? You're just a boy," he said. "Bring me the Golden Fleece, and then you can be king."

The Golden Fleece was a sheep's skin, and it was made of gold. Everyone knew the story. It was in a tree in a garden far away, and a man-eating dragon lived under the tree.

"The journey will be dangerous," Jason said. "The dragon guards the fleece night and day. Everyone knows that – but I will do it."

King Pelias smiled. "Jason is strong but stupid," he thought. "He's going to die, and I'll still be king."

"Good luck," he said in a loud voice.

"Thank you, Uncle," said Jason. "I'm going to take a few friends with me."

"Take as many friends as you want," said King Pelias.

Luckily, Jason knew all the most famous heroes in Greece. He sent messages to ask for their help, and fifty heroes came to row his ship and fight for him. Their ship's name was the *Argo*, so they called themselves the Argonauts.

Zetes and **Calais** were the sons of the North Wind. They could fly.

Orpheus had the most beautiful singing voice.

Heracles was the strongest man in the world.

Theseus was a famous monster killer.

Atalanta was the fastest runner in the world.

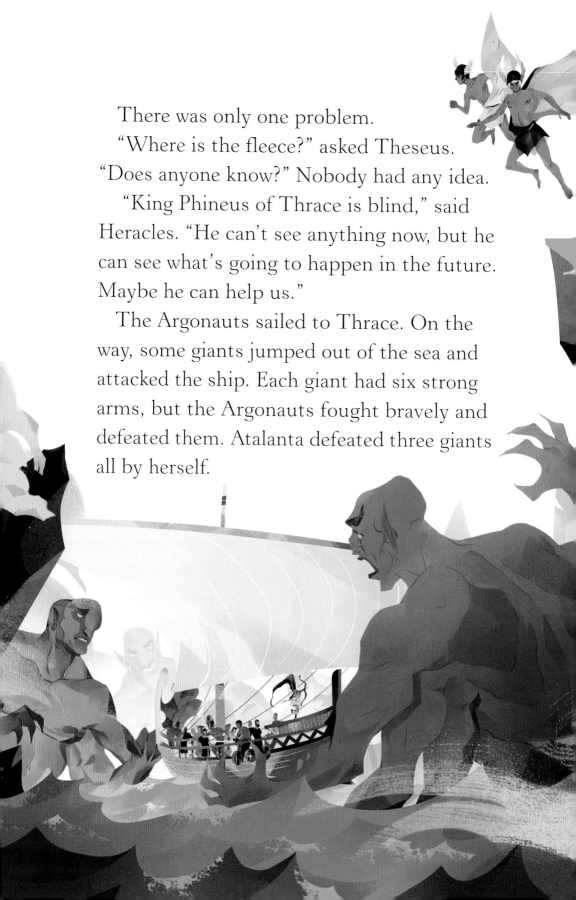

There was only one problem.

"Where is the fleece?" asked Theseus. "Does anyone know?" Nobody had any idea.

"King Phineus of Thrace is blind," said Heracles. "He can't see anything now, but he can see what's going to happen in the future. Maybe he can help us."

The Argonauts sailed to Thrace. On the way, some giants jumped out of the sea and attacked the ship. Each giant had six strong arms, but the Argonauts fought bravely and defeated them. Atalanta defeated three giants all by herself.

When they arrived in Thrace, the city was empty. King Phineus lived alone in a ruined palace. Every day, horrible bird-monsters flew down and ate all his food. They were called the Harpies. King Phineus was always hungry.

The Argonauts decided to help the king. First they cooked an enormous meal and put it outside the palace. Then they hid behind some rocks.

When the Harpies flew down to eat the
food, the heroes jumped out of their hiding
places. The Harpies tried to fly away, but
Zetes and Calais flew faster. They caught
the monsters and brought them down to the
ground. Heracles, Theseus and the other
heroes held swords to the Harpies' necks.

"Wicked monsters!" said Jason. "Go away
and never come back!"

The Harpies left Thrace immediately.
King Phineus was so happy that he danced
around the rocks.

"You have saved my life!" he said. "What can I do for you?"

"Where can we find the Golden Fleece?" asked Jason. "Please, tell us."

King Phineas stopped smiling. "Are you sure? The journey will be terrible, and that dragon will kill you. You should try something easier."

"I have to do this," said Jason. "If I can bring back the Fleece, I will be King of Thessaly."

"Then you should sail to Colchis, a country on the Black Sea. But you must be careful of the Crashing Rocks."

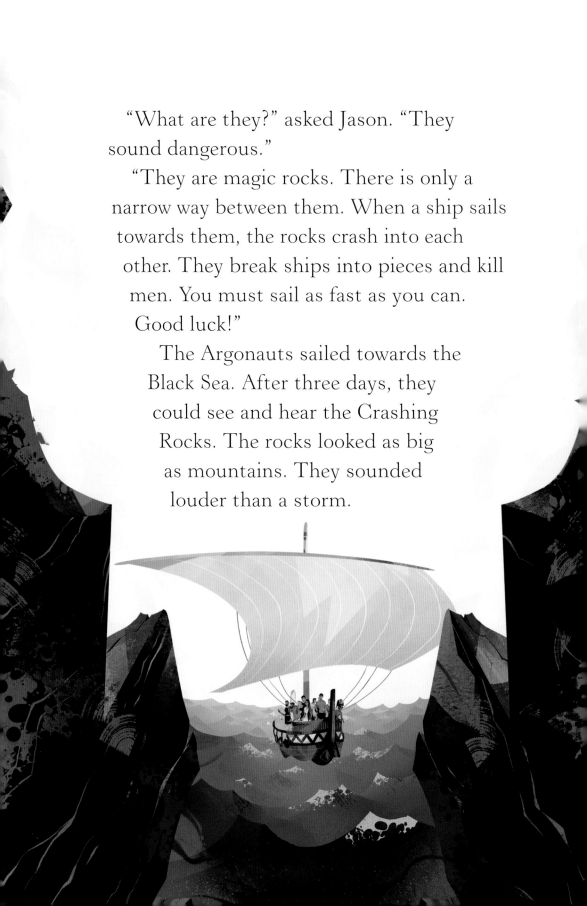

"What are they?" asked Jason. "They sound dangerous."

"They are magic rocks. There is only a narrow way between them. When a ship sails towards them, the rocks crash into each other. They break ships into pieces and kill men. You must sail as fast as you can. Good luck!"

The Argonauts sailed towards the Black Sea. After three days, they could see and hear the Crashing Rocks. The rocks looked as big as mountains. They sounded louder than a storm.

"We will not die today," shouted Jason. "We will row for our lives!"

Orpheus began to sing. His song was beautiful, and the Argonauts felt braver. Now the fifty Argonauts rowed faster than five hundred men.

The enormous rocks started to move.

"Faster!" shouted Jason. The ship moved quickly forward.

With Orpheus' song in their ears, the Argonauts rowed faster than the wind.

The rocks crashed together, but the ship was already safe on the other side.

"We did it!" roared Heracles.

The Argonauts sang while they rowed into the dark, dangerous waters of the Black Sea. They sailed through terrible storms, and past islands full of monsters. One night, wicked metal birds attacked the *Argo*, but the Argonauts defeated them.

At last they arrived in Colchis. King Aeetes was not pleased when he saw the Argonauts outside his palace gates.

"We have come to fetch the Golden Fleece," Jason explained.

King Aeetes was afraid of the Argonauts. He was too frightened to say no to Jason, but he didn't want to give him the Fleece.

"If you do three tasks for me, the Fleece will be yours," he said. "First, you must harness my bulls. Second, you must break the ground in my field. Third, you must plant the field with dragons' teeth."

"That doesn't sound too difficult," said Jason. "My Argonauts will help me."

"Oh, no!" said King Aeetes. "You must do the tasks alone. You can start in the morning."

King Aeetes gave the Argonauts a feast. Servants lit fires, and carried out enormous plates of meat. Orpheus sang happy songs. The Argonauts ate well, and then went to sleep in the palace.

In the middle of the night, the king's daughter, Medea, came to find Jason.

"Listen," she whispered. "My father is going to trick you. His three tasks are impossible. The bulls will breathe fire. If you plant dragons' teeth in the ground, soldiers will grow instead of plants. You are strong, Jason, but not strong enough. You are going to die."

Medea was very beautiful. "I'll show her that I'm brave," thought Jason. "I'm not afraid," he said.

"You *should* be afraid," said Medea, "but
I can help you. Take this magic ointment
and put it on your skin tomorrow. No fire or
metal will hurt you all day." She gave Jason a
small pot.

"Thank you," said Jason. "Why are you
helping me?"

The princess didn't answer. She was
already gone.

In the morning, Jason put on the ointment, and then he went outside. King Aeetes was waiting for him. "Look at those bulls!" he roared.

The two black bulls were enormous. They breathed fire from their mouths, and burned the grass around their feet. Their metal horns were as long as swords.

"Are you sure about this, Jason?" asked Heracles quietly. The big man looked worried.

"Of course I am!" said Jason. He ran straight at the bulls, and held their horns so that they couldn't move. Their fire was all around him, but it didn't hurt him. With the magic ointment, he was safe.

"Down!" shouted Jason. He was so strong that he pushed both the bulls to the ground. Now they were frightened of him, and Jason harnessed them easily.

Jason looked for Medea and saw her in the crowd. She smiled at him.

King Aeetes wasn't smiling. "Why isn't this man dead?" he wondered.

Now Jason was driving the bulls around the field. The crowd roared. They were enjoying this.

"This isn't a game!" shouted King Aeetes. "Finish your task!"

Jason carefully drove the bulls in a straight line, up and down the field. They broke the ground and turned the earth over. The bulls did everything that he wanted.

All the Argonauts were amazed.

"How did you do that?" asked Theseus. Heracles tried to touch a bull. Its hot breath burned his hand, and everyone laughed.

Jason was sad because he couldn't see Medea. Then suddenly she appeared beside him. "Medea!" Jason smiled. "Did you see that? What did you think?"

"Shh!" she whispered. "My father is watching, so I have to hurry. When the soldiers start growing, you must throw stones at them."

"What? What do you mean?" asked Jason – but the princess was gone.

King Aeetes was waiting for Jason. With a wicked smile, he gave the young hero a bag full of dragons' teeth.

"You are doing well," he said. "Just throw these over the broken ground. Then you can have the Golden Fleece."

Jason walked around the field. He threw white dragons' teeth across the dark earth. They looked like little stars.

In the places where they fell, men started to grow out of the earth. They all had swords, and they were shouting angrily.

Soon hundreds of soldiers were in the field around Jason. They tried to fight him, but their swords couldn't hurt him. Medea's ointment was still strong.

Jason picked up a stone and threw it into the crowd of soldiers.

It hit one of them. "Who threw that?" he said.

"He did," said Jason. He pointed at another soldier.

The two soldiers started fighting each other. Jason threw another stone, and then another.

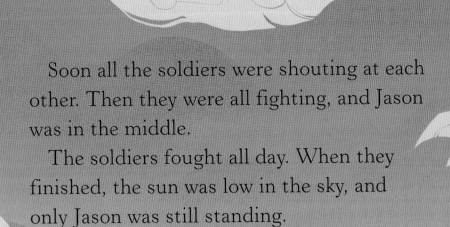

Soon all the soldiers were shouting at each
other. Then they were all fighting, and Jason
was in the middle.

The soldiers fought all day. When they
finished, the sun was low in the sky, and
only Jason was still standing.

"King Aeetes, I have finished all your
tasks," said Jason.

King Aeetes was angry. "You can have the
Fleece in the morning," he shouted, and he
ran back to the palace.

The Argonauts lit a fire and had a feast by the sea. Servants brought food and drink down from the palace, but before the Argonauts could drink anything, Medea ran up to them.

"Don't drink from those bottles," she said. "If you do, you will fall asleep, and then my father will kill you all."

"Thank you, Medea!" said Jason. "You've saved my life again. What can I do for you?"

Medea looked up at him. "Take me away from here," she whispered. "I hate this place."

"Of course!" Jason was so happy that he wanted to sing. "But I must take the Fleece, too."

"Don't worry," said Medea. "I have an idea. Follow me, and bring those bottles."

Jason followed her into the darkness. Medea held his hand. They walked around the palace and came to a quiet garden.

They saw a bright light, high in the leaves of a tree. It was shining like the sun.

"The Fleece!" whispered Jason.

"There's the dragon, too," said Medea. She pointed to the bottom of the tree.

Now Jason saw the monster. It had enormous yellow eyes, and it was watching him.

"Quick! Throw a bottle into its mouth," said Medea.

Jason threw one bottle and then another. The dragon roared, and broke the bottles in its long teeth. Soon it was asleep.

Jason quickly climbed the tree and took the Fleece, and then he and the princess went back to the feast.

Very early the next morning, Jason and the Argonauts sailed away from Colchis. They took Medea with them. When King Aeetes woke up, they were already far away. His Golden Fleece and his daughter were gone.

Their journey home was long and difficult, but finally they arrived back in Thessaly. King Pelias wasn't expecting them at all. When Jason walked into the palace, the king tried to hide, but Jason soon found him.

"I have brought the Fleece, Uncle," he said. "And I have found my queen!" He held Medea's hand.

King Pelias didn't try to argue. He ran away and no one ever saw him again.

The Argonauts feasted for a whole week. Zetes and Calais flew up into the roof with the Golden Fleece, and it shone down on the crowd. Orpheus' music made everyone dance. Heracles played strong-man games with Theseus, and Atalanta defeated everyone at running.

Jason and Medea became King and Queen of Thessaly, and the other heroes sailed back to their homes.

This all happened many years ago, but no one has ever forgotten the brave story of Jason and the Argonauts.

About the story

Thousands of years ago in Greece, people came together to tell stories about proud kings and queens and brave heroes. The story of Jason and the Argonauts was one of them. There were no books of stories then. Instead, storytellers listened to the stories, then remembered them and told other people.

The land of Colchis was where the country of Georgia is now, by the Black Sea. 2,500 years ago, people in this area used to put sheep's fleeces in rivers. The fleeces caught tiny pieces of gold in the water. When the fleeces dried, people could collect the gold. Perhaps the idea of the Golden Fleece came from this.

On the right is a picture of a Greek vase, showing the story of Jason.

The Argonauts

Choose the right sentence ending for each hero.

Zetes...

Jason...

Atalanta...

Heracles...

Orpheus...

A. ...defeated three giants on the way to Thrace.

B. ...brought the Harpies down to the ground.

C. ...sang to make the Argonauts feel braver.

D. ...grew up poor and angry, far away from home.

E. ...tried to touch one of King Aeetes's bulls.

Mixed-up story

Can you put these pictures and sentences in order?

A.

The Crashing Rocks sounded louder than a storm.

B.

Fifty heroes came to row Jason's ship and fight for him.

C.

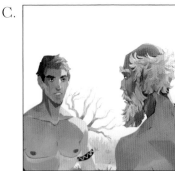

"You have saved my life What can I do for you?"

D.

"Wicked monsters! Go away and never come back!"

E.

At last they arrived in Colchis.

F.

King Phineas lived alone in a ruined palace.

G.

On the way, some giants jumped out of the sea.

H.

"Bring me the Golden Fleece."

I.

The ship was safe on th other side.

Which is true?

Choose the right sentence for each picture.

1.

2.

A. King Pelias thinks Jason is strong but stupid.

B. King Pelias thinks Jason is brave and clever.

A. King Aeetes is excited to meet the Argonauts.

B. King Aeetes is not pleased to see the Argonauts.

3.

4.

A. Medea is going to trick Jason.

B. Medea just wants to leave Colchis.

A. The bull's breath burns Jason's body.

B. With the magic ointment, Jason is safe.

The tasks

Choose the best word to finish the sentence.

1.

The two black bulls ....
fire from their mouths.

tasted   noticed   breathed

2.

Jason carefully .... the
bulls in a straight line.

drove   followed   turned

3.

Men started to ....
out of the earth.

escape   grow   shout

4.

Only Jason was still ....

winning   missing   standing

The Golden Fleece

Choose *one* word from the list to finish each sentence.

> away by down from in into

1.

The Argonauts had another feast .... the sea.

2.

"Take me away .... here."

3.

They saw a light, high .... the leaves of a tree.

4.
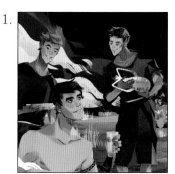

"Throw a bottle .... its mouth."

5.

King Pelias ran ....

6.

The Golden Fleece shone .... on the crowd.

Word list

attack (v) if you attack someone, you start a fight with them or try to hurt them.

blind (adj) if you are blind, you can't see anything.

bull (n) a male cow.

breathe (v) to take in air through your nose and mouth. You need to breathe to stay alive. Your **breath** (n) is the air that you take in and push out.

crashing (adj) when something crashes, it hits something else suddenly, with a loud noise.

crowd (n) lots of people together in one place.

defeat (v) when you defeat someone, you win a fight or a competition against them.

dragon (n) an animal in stories with a long body, wings and a tail. Dragons sometimes breathe fire.

earth (n) you grow plants in earth. Usually it is a thick brown powder.

feast (n) a really good meal with a lot of food.

fleece (n) the skin and wool of a sheep.

future (n) the time to come.

guard (n) a soldier who protects a person or a place.

harness (n, v) you put a harness on a horse or a cow when you want it to pull something.

horn (n) some animals, like cows and goats, have horns on either side of their head. Horns are hard and sharp.

journey (n) when you travel from one place to another, you make a journey.

narrow (adj) the opposite of wide.

ointment (n) a kind of medicine that you put on your skin to make it better, or so that it feels better.

plant (v) to put a seed in the ground so that it grows.

roar (v) when a wild animal is angry, it roars. When people roar, they shout loudly.

row (v) to move a boat forward in the water using long wooden paddles called oars.

ruined (adj) when a building is ruined, it is broken and spoiled.

sail (v) when you sail a ship, you use a sail – a large piece of cloth – to catch the wind and push the ship forward.

save someone's life (v) if someone is going to die and you make sure that they live, you save their life.

servant (n) someone who works for another person, especially in their home.

task (n) something that you have to do.

uncle (n) your uncle is your father's brother or your mother's brother.

whisper (v) when you say something very, very quietly, you whisper.

Answers

The Argonauts

Heracles – E

Jason – D

Zetes – B

Atalanta – A

Orpheus – C

Mixed-up story

H, B, G, F, D,
C, A, I, E

Which is true?

1. A
2. B
3. B
4. B

The tasks

1. breathed
2. drove
3. grow
4. standing

The Golden Fleece

1. by
2. from
3. in
4. into
5. away
6. down

You can find information about other Usborne English Readers here:
www.usborneenglishreaders.com

Designed by Melissa Gandhi

Series designer: Laura Nelson Norris

Edited by Mairi Mackinnon

Page 32: Greek vase showing Jason conquering the Golden Fleece
with Medea's help © Photo Scala, Florence

First published in 2019 by Usborne Publishing Ltd.,
Usborne House, 83-85 Saffron Hill, London EC1N 8RT, England.
www.usborne.com Copyright © 2019 Usborne Publishing Ltd.